PLANETARY GODS & GODDESSES
Coloring Book

Astronomy & Myths of the New Solar System

☆ ☆ ☆

M. KELLEY HUNTER

Our New Solar System

Astronomers are discovering more and more planetoids in the far reaches of our solar system. These new distant neighbors are being named for lesser-known gods and goddesses from around the world. Many planets have familiar names from Greek and Roman mythology. New ones are from Hawai'i, India, and Lithuania, from the Inuit, Etruscan, Rapa Nui, Tongva, Wayu'u, and Iroquois peoples, and even from J.R.R. Tolkien's prehistory of Middle Earth. This book introduces mythic images and their storylines. A global map shows their geographical origins. Sky maps and tables give basic astronomy information.

Copyright 2016 by Kelley Hunter, HELIA Productions
ISBN: 978-0-9976540-0-4

Illustrations by the author, with much early design work and inspiration from Dipali Dutta.

Solar system map and cover enhancement by Dana Hunt.

Front cover illustration colored by Anne Jameson. If you imagine a different way to color this image, gather your pencils, markers, or crayons and turn to page 29.

Cover and interior design and layout and book production by Kate Mueller, Pendragon Productions.

Contact the publisher for group packages and for slide show presentations on the new solar system in person, via Skype, or as webinars. www.heliastar.com.

Look for storybooks in the growing **Stories in the Stars** series for the young and the older, telling more about the gods and goddesses of the new solar system. To be on our mailing list to receive email announcements, sign up on the *Cosmic News* list at www.heliastar.com and visit her Facebook page, Kelley Hunter, AstroMythology. If you are interested in astrology, know that all these new objects in the solar system can be inserted into your birth chart and interpreted. Contact the author for this service, via her website.

What's Inside

Urania, muse of astronomy, from old print.

☆ 3 ☆

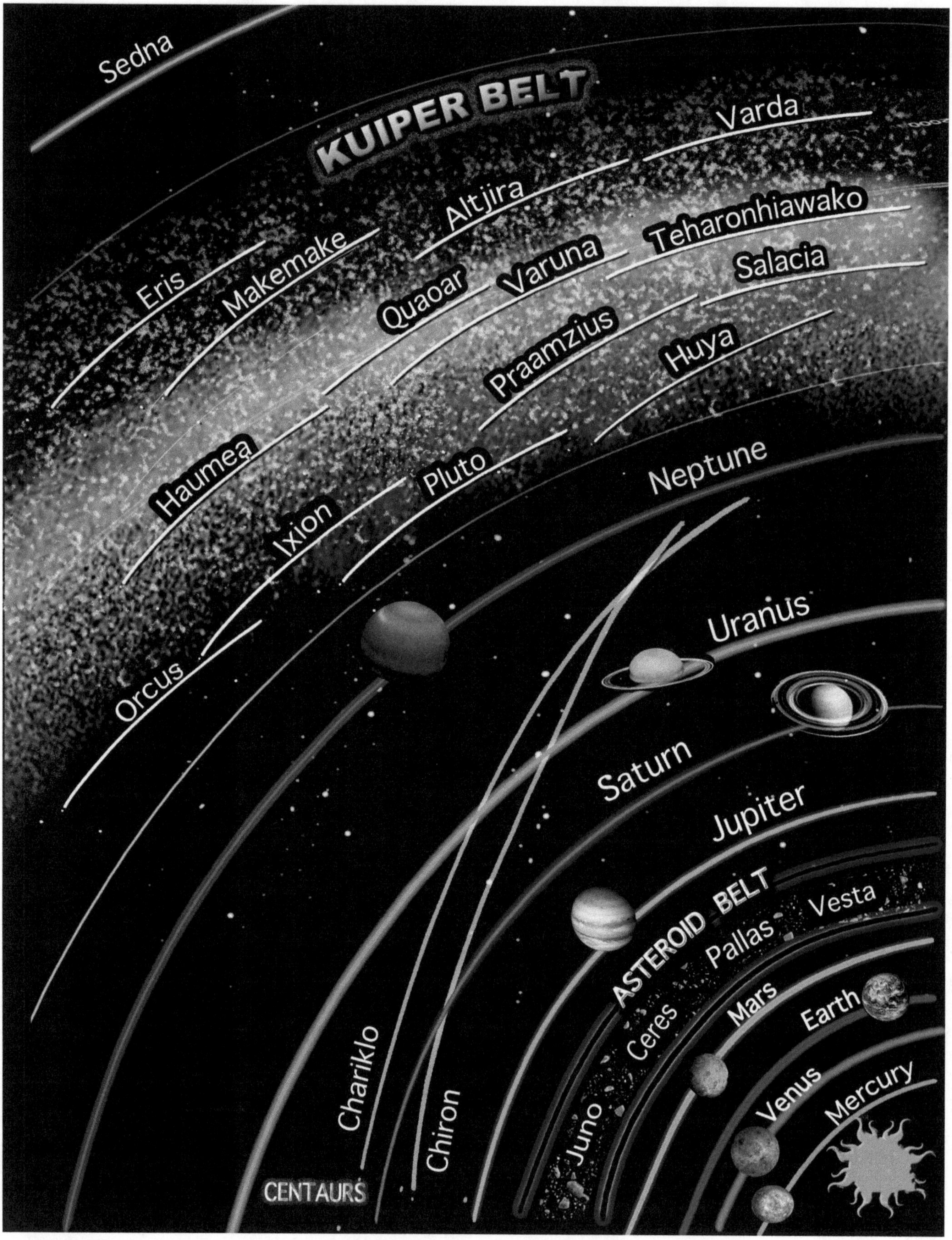

Sedna

KUIPER BELT

Varda

Altjira

Makemake   Teharonhiawako

Eris   Quaoar   Varuna   Salacia

Praamzius   Huya

Haumea   Pluto   Neptune

Ixion

Uranus

Orcus

Saturn

Jupiter

ASTEROID BELT   Vesta

Pallas

Ceres   Mars   Earth

Chariklo   Juno   Venus   Mercury

Chiron

CENTAURS

Astromythology

We live under a sky full of sparkling stars and circling planets, both a cosmic clock and a library. People all over the world tell stories about the stars to feel a connection to the heavens above. Today, with advanced telescopes and technology, our vision of the universe is expanding. Our solar system has stretched beyond the familiar planets we can see, named for Greco-Roman gods. More and more celestial objects are being discovered, both surprisingly near and far out in the dark cold distances. Astronomers recognize their responsibility when choosing names for heavenly bodies, using their knowledge of the skies gained through generations. Following tradition, they use names of gods and goddesses. In this third millennium, more of these names are drawn from different cultures around the world. We hear stories of gods and goddesses that may be new to us, exciting our imaginations and global understanding.

In this coloring book we journey through the solar system, visiting familiar planetary characters and meeting many new ones—*moving outward in order of their distance from the sun.* Creating the illustrations took a lot of research to learn about the stories and the people who wrote them. Please note that the coloring pages are not images from the cultures for whom these gods had divine meaning but were created with respect and a deep desire to connect with the wisdom of these gods and goddesses, arising anew to our attention. We need these original creator gods as we head further into this third millennium! Not all new planetoids have been in-

Urania, muse of astronomy. She is pictured using an armillary sphere, an ancient astronomical instrument. Various models were used by Greek, Islamic, and Chinese sky watchers. From illustration in Popular Astronomy *by N.C. Flammarion, 1879.*

cluded. The astronomy information in this book is current as of the 2016 publication date. Things changes fast in outer space, as surprising discoveries continue to be made.

Read about the mythic stories and find more astronomical information in the back of this book, starting on page 67.

Have Fun Coloring!

Colored pencils and watercolor pencils are recommended. You can use watercolors with brushes, magic markers, and whatever else you want. So that colors don't bleed through, especially from magic markers, I suggest you place a piece of heavy paper behind the page you are coloring. You don't have to color every little thing and you don't have to stay in the lines! Just have fun.

Amaterasu

MERCURY

Venus

GAIA EARTH

CERES

PALLAS & JUNO

SATURN

Chiron ♥ Chariklo

URANUS ♡ GAIA

NEPTUNE

SALACIA

HAUMEA

Planet 9 _____

(Make up a name!)

There is an undiscovered ninth planet way far out, beyond Sedna. What does Planet 9 look like? Who lives on it? Does it have moons or rings? What is its name? What god or goddess is associated with it? Draw it here.

Planet 9

Describe and write the story of undiscovered Planet 9 here.

_____

_____

_____

_____

_____

_____

_____

_____

_____

_____

_____

_____

_____

_____

_____

_____

_____

_____

My Planet_____

(Make up a name!)

Make up your own planet! What does your planet look like? Who lives on it? Does it have moons or rings? What is its name? What god or goddess is associated with it? Draw it here.

My Planet

Describe and write the story of your planet.

_____

_____

_____

_____

_____

_____

_____

_____

_____

_____

_____

_____

_____

_____

_____

_____

_____

The New Solar System

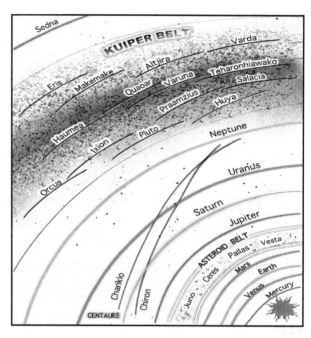

The Sun is our life-giving star, center of our solar system. Planets, near and far, circle the Sun. Like an orchestra leader, the Sun conducts the many planets and bodies that circle in their orbits, celestial musicians playing their instruments in what has been called the Harmony of the Spheres.

Classical Planets, Mercury through Saturn, are visible to our unaided sight.

Asteroids, also called minor planets, orbit in a broad band between Mars and Jupiter, leftovers from a planet shattered long ago. Starting in 1801 with the discovery of Ceres, hundreds of thousands have been discovered, from 20 to 590 miles (32–950 kilometers) in diameter. Ceres is rounded and has been reclassified as a dwarf planet. The rest have odd, irregular shapes. A few have moons. The composition of Vesta suggests it almost became a planet. Asteroid names come from many cultures and mythologies, geographical places, and celebrity and personal names. One is likely to have your name!

Centaur Objects are part asteroid, part comet, named for the mythic Greek figures that are half horse and half human. This category includes thousands of small rocky objects with irregular, unstable orbits that cross the paths of other planets. They may be temporary visitors to our solar system.

The **Outer Planets**, Uranus and Neptune, were discovered by mathematics and telescopes in 1781 and 1845.

Trans-Neptunian Objects (TNOs) orbit largely beyond Neptune. This large category includes objects in three main divisions: the Kuiper Belt, the scattered disk, and the largely unknown Oort Cloud.

Kuiper (ky-per) **Belt Objects** (KBOs) include millions of tiny icy TNOs that orbit the Sun in a broad band of space. Pluto is one of the closest. Most have irregular shapes. Some have moons or companion objects. Subcategories include: (1) **Plutinos**, which orbit the Sun in a dance with Neptune. For instance, Pluto orbits the Sun two times for every three orbits of Neptune, 2:3; others may have a different rhythm, perhaps 3:4. (2) **Cubewanos** (Q-B-1-Os) are farther away and not in such a dance with Neptune.

Dwarf Planets are round and have some space around them. Ceres in the Asteroid Belt, as well as Pluto, Haumea, Eris, and Makemake in the Kuiper Belt, are in this category. As we learn more, additional objects may be reclassified as dwarf planets.

Stories in the Stars

The Sun, Our Star

There are many Sun gods and goddesses around the world. Here are two.

HELIOS (hee'-lee-ohs)   *page 7*
The Sun god of Greece drives the chariot of the Sun across the sky each day. Helios is from the older generation of gods before classical Apollo, perhaps from Egypt, where the Sun god was honored in an ancient city the Greeks called Heliopolis, City of the Sun. Here we see Helios using a looking glass to peer into the future.

AMATERASU (ah-mah-tare-ah-soo)   *page 9*
This ancient Japanese Sun goddess emerges from her cave after the winter solstice, the darkest time of the year, and sees her own light reflected in a mirror. Here she turns the mirror toward you. The Sun disc of Amaterasu is the main symbol on the Japanese flag. Japan has long been called the Land of the Rising Sun. See her name in Japanese on the lower left of the drawing.

Classical Planets: Small and Rocky

MERCURY   *page 11*
The messenger of the gods, Hermes in Greek, zooms around the Sun, appearing to move back and forth from our point of view. This trickster god likes to play games. Wearing winged cap and sandals, he carries a healing staff with serpents winding around it called a caduceus.

VENUS   *page 13*
The goddess of love and beauty was born from sea foam. With her irresistible charm, she expresses the wisdom of the heart. In the color and scent of flowers, she shows us the beauty of life. Her bird is the dove. Never too high in the sky, planet Venus is the brightest, seen as the morning or evening star.

GAIA (guy'-uh)   *page 15*
The Earth goddess is the bountiful mother who provides all we need to live on our home planet. As she takes care of us, let us take care of her. Grandmother Moon circles Earth, waxing and waning each month, as she moves the ocean tides and the daily rhythms of life.

MARS   *page 17*

Warrior and hero, Mars is strong and courageous. He protects and defends. He is the go-getter, the competitor and sports champion, and the hunter (here with a falcon). Spacecraft have landed on our next-door planet and sent back pictures of its strange, desert-like landscape. Tracking the orbit of Mars helped astronomer Johannes Kepler realize that planetary orbits are elliptical, not circular. Its two tiny moons are named for the companions of the classic god of war—Deimos, which means "fear," and Phobos, "panic."

Asteroids

Following are the first four asteroids discovered, ordered according to distance from the Sun, from nearest to farthest, and numbered according to when they were discovered: Ceres discovered first (1801). Vesta discovered last (1807).

VESTA (ves'-tah): Asteroid 4   *page 19*

The priestess of the sacred fire has a quiet glow about her. She is the brightest of the asteroids. Eldest sister of the Olympian gods, Vesta is honored for her loving devotion in the circle of home and hearth. She also creates an uplifting sanctuary in places of worship—temple, church, cathedral, mosque, synagogue, or sacred site in nature. Her flowers are the poppy and angel trumpet. Her Greek name is Hestia.

CERES (seer'-eez): Asteroid 1   *page 21*

The goddess of grain feeds her people, body and soul, according to the seasons and the fruits of the land. First discovered and the largest object in the asteroid belt, Ceres is round and has been reclassified as a dwarf planet. Like a celestial shepherdess, she tends her huge flock of asteroids. Demeter is her Greek name.

PALLAS (pal'-ass): Asteroid 2   *page 23*

The goddess of wisdom, also known as Athena, is the daughter of Jupiter. Two of her gifts to humans were the olive tree and the art of weaving. She was crafty and strategic in times of war and peace. Her bird is the wise owl. She carries a shield showing the head of snake-haired Medusa, who turned men to stone. Pallas aided Perseus in cutting off the head.

JUNO (joo'-no): Asteroid 3   *page 23*

The queen goddess is the wife of Jupiter and gracious hostess on Mount Olympus, home of the gods. The peacock, with its fantail and all-seeing eyes, is her bird: "The night has a thousand eyes." She used them to spy on Jupiter who had many girlfriends. Her Greek name is Hera.

Classical Planets: Large and Gaseous

JUPITER   *page 25*

King of the gods, the Thunderer reigns on Mount Olympus. His Greek name is Zeus. This powerful god imposes justice and maintains order and good will. Ask him for boons and favors. His bird is the keen-sighted eagle. Jupiter has sixty-seven discovered moons. Large and small, they are named for the many goddesses, nymphs, and mortal women in Jupiter's stories. Ganymede, Europa, Io, and Callisto were seen by Galileo using an early telescope. They are called the Galilean moons. On this page you can design Jupiter's many moons.

SATURN   *page 27*

The god of time, ancient of days, is a Titan of the older generation of gods. His Greek name is Chronos. He enforces cosmic law and defines boundaries with his planet's wide rings. He uses his sharp sickle to reap the harvest and to end all things in the ultimate test of time, throughout great cosmic cycles. "There is a time to every purpose under heaven."

The Centaurs

Most centaurs in mythology were rough and ready characters but not these two.

CHIRON (ky'-ron)   *page 29*

This wise Greek centaur was a revered healer and teacher of many young heroes, including Hercules. Son of Saturn and a water nymph, he lived in a cave on Mount Pelion. Accidentally wounded by a poisoned arrow, he could not heal himself. He gave up his mortal life to become the starry constellation Centaurus. That constellation's brightest star, Alpha Centauri, is the closest star to our solar system. Here we see Chiron teaching Achilles how to shoot a bow and arrow. The image is taken from a mural in the Boston Museum of Fine Arts by American artist John Singer Sargent.

CHARIKLO (kar'-ih-klo)   *page 29*

Shown with Chiron, this river mermaid lived in the valley waters that meandered to the sea. She liked to sun herself on river rocks, watching Chiron from afar, admiring his noble form. He always noticed when she was nearby. They came to love each other, so she changed her shape from half fish to half horse to be with him, becoming one of the few female centaurs. In 2014, astronomers were surprised to discover that tiny Chariklo has two narrow rings, like a double halo.

Outer Planets: Telescopic and Gaseous

URANUS (your'-ah-nus)   *page 31*

This ancient primal sky god charges the atmosphere with electricity that brings lightning and thunderstorms, as well as earthquakes. He loved Earth goddess Gaia. Together they brought forth a new generation of gods, the Titans, as well as the one-eyed Cyclops. His son Saturn finally dethroned him. Ouranos is his Greek name. This planet's seventeen moons were named for Shakespearean characters.

NEPTUNE   *page 33*

The god of the sea stirs up the oceans with his mighty trident, creating waves and sea breezes, storms and hurricanes. He rules over all sea creatures, including mermaids and mermen, calling them with his conch shell horn. He rides a whale or a chariot pulled by sea horses. Poseidon is his Greek name. In this illustration of Neptune, you will see Salacia.

Kuiper Belt Objects/Trans-Neptunian Objects

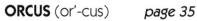

SALACIA (sal-ay'-ah-shah)   *page 33*

This goddess of the saltwater creates sparkles on the calm, sunlit sea. Neptune wanted to marry her, but she did not believe him and went away. Neptune sent a dolphin, Delphinus, to convince her that he was truly in love. In our picture, the dolphin brings a large lustrous pearl as a gift from Neptune. Astronomically, Salacia is a Kuiper Belt Object, discovered in 2004.

ORCUS (or'-cus)   *page 35*

This Etruscan underworld god of ancient Italy punishes oath breakers. The one moon of Orcus is named for Vanth, a winged female with a torch to guide departing souls to his realm. In J. R. R. Tolkien's The Lord of the Rings, the scary orcs were named for him. We are also reminded of the intelligent orca, largest of the deep-diving dolphins. Our image shows the Mouth of Orcus, a sculpture in the Park of Monsters in Bomarzo, Italy. An inscription reads "All thoughts fly." You can go in—if you dare.

PLUTO *page 37*

Pluto, or Hades, the god of death and rebirth, lives in underground caverns guarded the the three-headed dog Cerberus. Dark and mysterious, he rarely visits the upper world and even then wears a helmet that makes him invisible. Souls of the dead are taken across the River Styx into his realm by Charon, the ferryman. Charon is the name of the largest moon of dwarf planet Pluto, almost half its size. Is this a double planet? Pluto has four more tiny moons. The *New Horizons* spacecraft, the first to visit Pluto, sent back detailed photos in 2015, showing a heart-shaped formation on its surface.

IXION (iks'-see-on)   *page 39*

The king of the Lapiths, a tribe of ancient Greece, married Princess Dia, then killed her father. Ixion was outcast for this terrible crime. Jupiter finally agreed to give him a second chance, but instead Ixion flirted indecently with Juno, Jupiter's wife. The king of the gods was furious and had Ixion chained to a wheel rolling through the dark underworld, repeating over and over, "Show gratitude to your benefactor."

HUYA (hoo'-yah)   *page 41*

The rain god of the Wayu'u people brings needed water to their hot, dry peninsula on the north Caribbean coast of South American shared by Venezuela and Colombia. When selfish Howler Monkey King hoarded all the rain clouds, Huya stole his thunderbolts to return the rain to all the people. Kasipoluin, the Rainbow Serpent, announces the end of rainy season. Huya is said to live in celestial altitudes beyond the Sun. Now we see him there! His name is often spelled Juya.

PRAAMZIUS (prom'-zee-oos)   *page 43*

This ancient high god of Lithuania created the world and determines the fates of all beings. Ruler of Sky and Time, he is known to foster peace and friendship among the people. Our illustration is taken from a carved wooden figure on the Hill of Witches, a forest park with hundreds of such sculptures. He holds a symbol called a rune from the Baltic Sea area that means "hidden and mysterious," like destiny. The fire ceremony is one of the most important of Lithuania's ancient rituals, still performed by circles of women moving around a central flame. The page borders are designs from traditional sashes woven and worn by women.

VARUNA (vah-roo'-nah)   *page 45*

This Vedic god of cosmic harmony is the upholder of heaven and Earth, ruling oceans, rivers, and rain. Brother of the Sun, this creator god of ancient India uses the stars as eyes to see everywhere on Earth. Riding his crocodile-like *makara*, he uses a snake as a lasso to catch outlaws who break the cosmic laws. His other brother, a dragon, once drank up all the waters, causing global drought. Our dragon image shows the great sea dragon of the Indian Ocean. Varuna called on thunder god Indra for help in quelling the greedy dragon. In thanks, Varuna let Indra rule for thousands of years, but now he returns to help restore cosmic order on Earth once again. See his name in Sanskrit above the English.

HAUMEA (how-may'-ah)   *page 47*
This ancestral mother goddess of the Hawaiian Islands brings fertility to the land and its people, giving birth to all beings. She ever renews herself, surrounded by tropical fruits and flowers. The two moons of this dwarf planet are named for two of her daughters—sea goddess Namaka and Hi'iaka, goddess of the Hula dance. Volcano fire goddess Pele is also her daughter.

QUAOAR (kwah'-or)   *page 49*
The creative power of the Tongva people of the Los Angeles Basin is the original Formless One, who sang and danced the universe into being. Here we see Quaoar in more human form, dancing amidst cosmic fractals, strands of DNA, and Tongva petroglyph images, the codes of life. Quaoar first created Weywot, Sky Father, for whom the single moon of this dwarf planet is named. Next Chehooit, Earth Mother, was created, followed by the Sun, Moon, stars, and all creatures, great and small.

TEHARONHIAWAKO (tay-hah'-rone-hi-ah-wah'-ko)   *page 51*
The great-grandson of the Great Spirit of the Iroquois is descended from the Star People. He planted the first corn and sunflowers, placing one flower in the sky to give light as the Sun. The white pine is the sacred tree of this people of northeast North America, a continent they call Turtle Island. This planetoid has a companion, named for his twin brother Sawiskera, a skilled hunter but jealous and deceitful. Some of the images in this illustration are taken from bead work made by Haudenosaunee (haw-den-oh-saw'-nee) women of upstate New York, a tribe of the larger Iroquois nation.

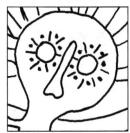

ALTJIRA (alt-jeer'-ah)   *page 53*
The Aboriginal creator god of the Arrernte people in central Australia emerged from the Great Dreaming. One story says that when he came down to create Earth and all its creatures, he walked with the feet of an emu bird. He soon retired back into the Great Dreaming, leaving other gods and spirits in charge. Much Aboriginal cave art dates back 50,000 years. This illustration depicts some *wandjina*, ancestor spirits, from cave drawings in western Australia.

MAKEMAKE (mah'-kay-mah'-kay)   *page 55*
This re-creative god-man presided over the Tangata Manu Birdman religion of the Rapa Nui people of remote Easter Island. Each year clan warriors descended a steep cliff and swam across a channel to bring back the first tern bird egg, representing new life. The winner's clan chief became king, as Makemake's earthly representative. This small Pacific island is known for its huge, carved stone statues called *moai* (mo'-eye), which honored the ancestors. Astronomically, Makemake is a dwarf planet.

VARDA (var'-dah)   *page 57*

The lady of the stars is goddess of the elves according to J.R.R. Tolkien's prehistory of Middle Earth. She kindled the stars to light up and designed many constellations. She created the Sun and Moon from the dew of Laurelin, the Tree of Gold, and Telperion, the Tree of Silver. She then set these great lights on their courses through the heavens. Varda has one moon, or companion object, named for Ilmare (ill-mar-ay'), her mythic handmaiden. There is also a KBO named for her husband, Manwe. You might recognize the Pleiades star cluster near the Moon.

ERIS (air'-iss *or* eer'-iss)   *page 59*

This goddess of discord stirs up jealousy and strife. Uninvited to a wedding feast, she tossed a golden apple to the guests, labeled "For the Fairest." A young man named Paris was asked to choose the fairest goddess. Juno offered him a kingdom; Pallas Athena great wisdom; but he chose Venus, who promised to give him Helen, the most beautiful woman in the world. This famous Judgment of Paris led to the tragic Trojan War. The one moon of dwarf planet Eris is named Dysnomia after her daughter, a demon of lawlessness.

SEDNA (sed'-nah)   *page 61*

The Inuit sea goddess lives at the bottom of the frigid Arctic Sea. Her story is tragic. She married a handsome stranger from across the seas. She soon discovered that he was a fearsome raven-man and called for help. When her father came to the rescue, Raven stirred up a storm. Afraid, her father pushed Sedna out of their kayak, cutting off her fingers when she tried to climb back on. She fell to the bottom of the sea. Her fingers and other body parts turned into sea creatures. Inuit shamans soothe Sedna to ensure a good sea hunt each year. Sedna is a TNO beyond the Kuiper Belt, far out toward the Oort Cloud.

PLANET 9   *page 63*

In 2016 astronomers realized there is a planet way far out, even beyond Sedna. What do you think it might be like? Does it have any moons? What would you name it? Suggestion: we don't have any planet names from Africa and few from Asia. Describe planet 9 on page 64.

MY PLANET   *page 65*

What does it look like? Who lives on it? What is its name? Does it have moons or rings? Draw a picture of it or the god or goddess associated with it. Write its story on page 66.

Geographical Map

Below are places of origin for names of solar system objects that are not Greco-Roman, identified by coloring book page numbers.

9	**Amaterasu**	Japan
35	**Orcus**	Etruscan Italy
41	**Huya**	Venezuela
43	**Praamzius**	Lithuania
45	**Varuna**	India
47	**Haumea**	Hawai'i
49	**Quaoar**	Los Angeles Basin
51	**Teharonhiawako**	Northeast North America crossing U.S.–Canada border
53	**Altjira**	Australia
55	**Makemake**	Easter Island
57	**Varda**	Tolkien's pre–Middle Earth (not shown!)
61	**Sedna**	Arctic Sea

Urania, muse of astronomy. From an engraving by J. Zucchi, after Angelina Kauffman, 1781.

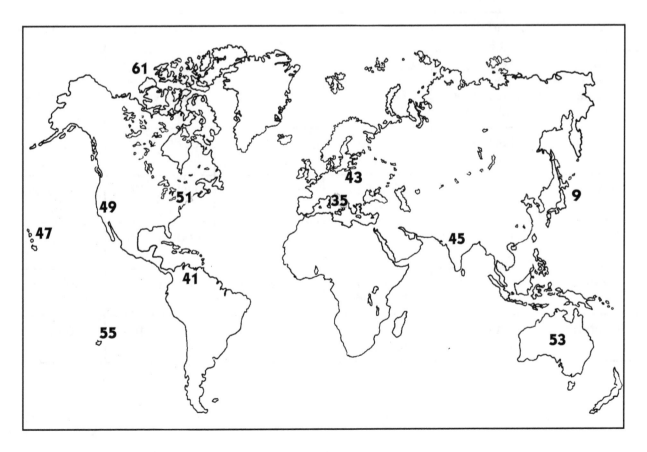

The Near Solar System

All of these bodies have names from Greco-Roman mythology. With more discoveries, the range of names has expanded. Many thousands of asteroids have names from cross-cultural myths and legends, as well as geographical and personal names. Note: The centaurs range in distance, crossing the orbits of Saturn, Uranus, Neptune, and even Pluto.

Name	Category	Diameter miles/ kilometers	Moons	Discovered	Orbit in Earth time
Mercury	Rocky Planet	3032m/4879km	none	easily visible	88 days
Venus	Rocky Planet	7521m/12104km	none	easily visible	243 days
Earth	Rocky Planet	7918m/12742km	one	home base	365 days
Mars	Rocky Planet	4221m/ 6792km	two	easily visible	687 days
Vesta	Asteroid 4	326m/525km	none	Mar 29, 1807	1325 days
Juno	Asteroid 3	143m/230km irregular shape	none	Sept 1, 1804	1595 days
Ceres	Dwarf Planet [Asteroid 1]	590m/950km	none	Jan 1, 1801	1680 days
Pallas	Asteroid 2	326m/524km	none	Mar 28, 1802	1686 days
Jupiter	Gas Planet, thin rings	88,881m/ 139,822km	67	easily visible	12 years
Saturn	Gas Planet, complex rings	72,367m/ 116,464km	62	easily visible	29 years
Chiron	Centaur Object thin ring	92-129m/ 148-208km	none	Nov 1, 1977	50+ years
Chariklo	Centaur Object two thin rings	160m/250km	none	Feb 15, 1997	62 years
Uranus	Gas Planet, thin rings	31,518m/ 50,724km	27	Mar 13, 1781	84 years
Neptune	Gas Planet, thin rings	30.599m/ 49,244km	14	Sept 23, 1846	165 years

The Far Solar System

Pluto is the largest at 1,473 miles/2,370 kilometers in diameter. Other new bodies are on the official roster; others await names. More are constantly discovered. Dates are from the Minor Planet Center of the International Astronomical Union. Some refer to plates (P) that show orbits only later identified (I) as objects.

TNO = Trans-Neptunian Object   KBO = Kuiper Belt Object

Name	Category	Origin	Moons	Discovered	Orbit in Earth time
Orcus	KBO/ Plutino	Etruscan Italy	one	Feb 17, 2004	247 years
Pluto	Dwarf Planet	Greco-Roman	five	Jan 23,1930 P Feb 18 1930 I	248 years
Ixion	KBO/ Plutino	Greece	none	May 22, 2001	256 years
Huya	KBO/ Plutino	Venezuela	none	Mar 10, 2000	256 years
Salacia	KBO	Roman	none	Sept 22, 2004	271 years
Praamzius	KBO	Lithuania	none	Jan 23, 2012	281 years
Varuna	KBO/Cubewano	India	none	Nov 28, 2000	283 years
Haumea	Dwarf Planet	Hawai'i	two	Mar 7, 2003 P Dec 28,2004 I	283 years
Quaoar	KBO/Cubewano	Tongva Los Angeles, CA	one	Jun 4, 2002	288 years
Teharonhiawako	KBO/ Cubewano	Iroquois, N.E. North America	one companion	Aug 20, 2001	295 years
Altjira	KBO/Cubewano	Aboriginal, Australia	one companion	Oct 20, 2001	297 years
Makemake	Dwarf Planet	Rapa Nui, Easter Island	none	Mar 31, 2005	310 years
Varda	KBO	J.R.R.Tolkien	one companion	Jun 21, 2003	311 years
Eris	Dwarf Planet	Greece	one	Oct 21, 2003 P Jan 5, 2005 I	557 years
Sedna	TNO	Inuit, Arctic Sea	none	Nov 14, 2003	11,400 years+-

About the Author

M. Kelley Hunter, PhD, has studied the sky as mythologist and stargazer since her teens. She has always loved mythic stories. Dazzled by the sparkling sky overhead, she led stargazing nights for many years for visitors to Maho Bay Campground, Caneel Bay Resort, and Friends of the VI National Park on St. John, Virgin Islands. Director of HELIA Productions, Kelley designs and cocreates multimedia and experiential presentations for a wide variety of groups and organizations. She enjoys the creative process as performer, visual artist, writer, and poet.

Contact Kelley via her website: www.heliastar.com.

Watch for more books in the growing Stories in the Stars series, for all ages.

Acknowledgments

Many more people contributed to this project than I can name. Here is a start.

Ari Chapin—his keen interest in my first sketch of the new astronomy map along with his sage advice informed me that his eight-year-old age group was a prime audience.

Jan Sandman fanned a glimmer of an idea into brighter inspiration.

Jim Eaton suggested a coloring book to introduce this material.

Dipali Dutta created essential early design work that prepared me for coloring book illustration. Feedback from artist friends was invaluable, especially Les Anderson, Gail Van De Bogurt, Dana Harrison, Joelen Mulvaney, and Kathleen Houlahan. Serious colorist Anne Jameson came along just in time for the cover image. Dana Hunt spent endless hours creating the solar system map, with her usual "wow" factor, and also enhanced the vibrancy of the cover image. Kate Mueller offered her creative flair to the book design even before I knew I needed her.

Special thanks to the Jaquith Public Library in Marshfield, Vermont, where I offered my first program on The New Solar System. Thanks to library director Susan Green and to children's librarian, Sylvia Smith, for significant feedback. I also thank the six enthusiastic members of the AstroMythology afterschool program: Jazmin, Wyatt, Jenn, Alice, Sam, and Aleacya.

Thanks to my Kickstarter supporters, and to the ladies at my coloring book tea parties for showing me how amazing the illustrations could look in color.

Printed in the USA
CPSIA information can be obtained
at www.ICGtesting.com
LVHW081056010424
776066LV00024B/465